CHURCH CHUCKLES

by CHARLES CARTWRIGHT

KREGEL PUBLICATIONS

Grand Rapids 6, Michigan

ABOUT CHURCH CHUCKLES

At first glance, the title Church Chuckles might seem a strange combination of words to describe a religious book. But if anyone has the right and the reason to "chuckle" now and then, it is the Christian. Charles Cartwright believes this and the popularity of his nationally syndicated cartoon feature has proved that many people agree with him.

Humor is not absent from the Bible narratives, nor is it missing in everyday Christian living. Many of the humorous incidents pictured in this series are all the more ludicrous because of their very similarity to real life. In fact, the cartoons of Charles Cartwright are justly famous for the faintly barbed truths they often portray. One sees himself on almost every page of this entertaining book — and finds himself "strangely warmed" with a desire to more effectively live the Christian life.

By means of his cartoons, Mr. Cartwright is able to cut right to the heart of the Christian life in an unusually effective way, imparting a challenge right along with the inevitable chuckle, reaching directly into the lives of young and old alike with the message of God's Word.

The Editors

FIRST PRINTING. . . . . MAY, 1960

SECOND PRINTING . . . . AUGUST, 1960

THIRD PRINTING. . . . . . AUGUST, 1963

" . . and so, THIS Sunday I have decided to preach on a less controversial subject. . ."

None of us enjoy being told our shortcomings. No minister relishes the necessity of risking offense. Yet our spiritual health is his primary duty. If, sometimes, we need a dose of bitter medicine to protect our physical health, we don't resent the doctor. Shouldn't this apply to the guardian of our spiritual health, too? .

**"You've certainly ruined my day with that ser-
mon about everybody being reunited in Heaven!"**

He shouldn't let his earthly experiences give him
the wrong idea about the hereafter. Another case
where a perfectly innocent sermon on a very general
subject unwittingly trod on sore toes. In this instance,
WHAT was said by the preacher, became something
totally different in the WAY it was interpreted by
this particular member. Maybe all preachers, to play
safe, should start their sermons with the protective
legal clause, "Any resemblance between my sermon
and any member of this congregation is purely coinci-
dental."

"Why don't you put in a golf course, Reverend? You should see the checks he writes for the Country Club."

Junior put his foot in his mouth . . . and his finger right on an important fact. For surveys prove that Mr. Average American spends a great deal more on recreational activities than he donates in support of his church. Having a certain amount of 'fun' is, of course, essential to a healthy mind and body. But should it occupy a place in our lives—and pocketbooks—several times the importance of our spiritual needs? Let's put first things FIRST!

"Fifteen definite converts, and one still doubt-ful."

The special mission offering is your opportunity to give one of the grandest of all gifts—the gift of light to those now immersed in heathen darkness. Missionaries throughout the world are dedicating their very lives to the spreading of the Word. You are only asked to give your money. Do what you can to help the vital work.

". . . so now let each give freely, generously, in accordance with what you reported on your income tax!"

Those who steer their daily lives in Christian principle are subject to the same tax burdens as others. Exposed to the same temptations to lighten that burden. Their strict accounting, however, is not prompted by fear of penalty. It is a natural expression of their desire to play fair with God and their fellow man.

"... and thank Thee for the peanut butter sand-wiches we are about to receive ..."

With or without the traditional 'turkey and trim-mings' most of us have ample cause for giving thanks. Not just on Thanksgiving Day, but every day of the year. And especially in these times of turmoil we need to keep our sense of perspective by counting our blessings frequently.

"Remember, Piffle's Posture Pews please particular people . . . and now, back to 'Sin Busters'!"

If the program of the church ever descends to this all-time low of crass commercialism, God pity us! Yet, sometimes in our efforts to generate enthusiasm apart from the Spirit of God, we stoop to almost as ridiculous a level of artificiality. Let us remember that only a divine visitation of the Holy Spirit can kindle the needed spark, holy zeal and enthusiasm — revival comes from God!

"Can't you be a little more quiet during church services?"

Habits have a way of undergoing radical change during vacation. Here is pictured an unfortunate conflict of diverse interests that need not have arisen if they had resolved the whole problem by going to church. Make it a point to attend church wherever your vacation takes you!

"He makes a wonderful example for the children. They live in daily fear of turning out like him!"

Perhaps a 'negative' example is better than none at all, but a positive one is assuredly the most beneficial to development of character. Many of us lose sight of what tremendous influences we have—for good or ill—upon our children. Influences that can MAKE or BREAK their lives—building the foundations of a rewarding and useful existence, or directing them toward selfish and unhappy years.

"And after I'd shown such **COMPLETE** faith—passing a gravel truck on a blind curve at ninety miles an hour!"

There's a vast difference between faith and foolhardiness. Failing to use the common sense our Creator gave us, we can hardly expect a chain of miracles to deliver us from deliberate folly. Faith gives access to courage, strength, and wisdom infinitely greater than our own—when we are in harmony with, and not opposing, God's laws.

"I feel **SO** good since we're tithing, Reverend! And with George's clever figuring of deductions and exemptions, we'll be giving less than before!"

Tithing is not only the responsibility but privilege of every Christian. Those who have made tithing a regular part of their life know there can be no exemptions or half-measures. Remove the word 'sacrificial' from the word 'giving', and much of the spirit of Christianity is lost.

"Too bad we can't enlist such talent for collecting overdue pledges!"

Stewardship is a privilege accorded God's people alone, the blood-bought ones. Should their response be an enforced submission or a glad surrender? This is a concept that goes far beyond monetary measure to envelop all that we are and have.

"When I get to the part about hellfire and brimstone shut off the air conditioning."

An unpopular message in today's churches—but one which must nonetheless be proclaimed by divine command. At the same time, this imaginary situation reveals another trend toward "comfortable" worship at the expense of sincerity and true devotion.

"If I'm as popular with my new congregation as you say, WHY have so few asked us to dinner?"

To get the answer, multiply two pieces of fried chicken times eight people. Joking aside, we all share one thing in common whatever our station in life . . . the desire to be 'accepted' by our fellow man. Some seek acceptance through wealth; some through power; but the Christian alone tries to be worthy of acceptance through unselfish service to God and man.

"He must've really told'em off today!"

Grim days like the present have a way of throwing into bold relief our shortcomings, whatever they be. Criticism hurts like iodine, but like iodine may reduce danger of worse complications. Every minister is faced with the dilemma of trying to say what he OUGHT to say in a way we would LIKE to hear. Let's give thanks for a minister with the courage to 'spank' us when we need it!

"Now here's the setup. Right after I announce the budget you soften 'em up with "Hearts and Flowers"; then I step in for the kill."

If our giving is no more systematic and sanctified than the offering about to be "lifted" in this church, how do we expect the Great Commission given by the Lord just before His Ascension to be carried out? Ours must be a wholehearted, all-out giving of time, talent and treasure to Him "Whose we are and Whom we serve"!

"You certainly gave us away—asking how much were the programs!"

An embarrassing moment; but soon forgotten. More important, it reveals this couple obviously has no church home. Could they but foresee the times of crisis ahead, which inevitably come to all—and know the comforting strength of a permanent church affiliation—one thing is sure. This very day would witness their commitment to its loving care, and a willing acceptance of their share of the accompanying responsibilities.

"The most inspiring sermon I ever heard . . . a turning point in my life . . . but did you have to keep us ten minutes overtime?"

This punctual minded member has no idea of the careful planning required to prune and trim a sermon to the demands of a rigid time schedule. So MUCH to say, so LITTLE time to say it. Is this selfsame member, we wonder, equally critical of himself when he slips into church ten or fifteen minutes late?

"Could you say grace during the half, Reverend? The game's all tied up seven to seven!"

Thanksgiving has come to mean, to many people little more than a day crowded with feasting, football games, and other leisure-time activities. Thanksgiving Day was originally dedicated by our forefathers as a day of worship and prayer, a day of giving thanks for deliverance from famine and peril.

"Better hadn't go pickin' on th' preacher's son. First he turns the other cheek—then 'Zowie'."

There are an awful lot of bullies in the world today who are doing their utmost to intimidate and frighten the Christian movement into a state of impotence. Like this preacher's son, many of us are learning that there comes a point beyond which meekness and submission spell ultimate disaster. Since the memorable day long ago when the money changers were driven from the Temple, the Christian has had to know not only when to meekly submit; but also when to courageously oppose.

"Guess we'll have to give up till later, Sarah. Every time you get to an interesting part, the preacher interrupts with his shouting!"

We wonder if these two 'visiting' ladies realize how difficult it is to deliver a sermon in the face of such distracting competition? Most sermons require at least twenty or thirty hours of preparation. Our courteous and undivided attention not only makes our minister's task infinitely more satisfying; but his message helps impart spiritual strength for the unknown trials we may face in the week lying ahead.

REV. TWEEDLE, D.D.

"**Lucky for you, traditions of the Cloth restrain me!**"

Lucky for us all—the restraint and moderation that characterizes every Christian community throughout our great land. We need not 'guess' what its absence would mean in its effect upon our environment. We can see—in another great nation of this Earth—how legalized violence and enslavement of the people ALWAYS follows abandonment of Christian ideals.

"Please, Gerald, not the church service! I look a fright!"

Television brings many famous religious personages into our living rooms. Their spiritual inspiration is a valuable adjunct to that which we gain from regular church attendance. If our love of ease, however, should ever tempt us to substitute 'TV church attendance' for the real thing, we would find our personal fellowship with God had become a hollow and meaningless thing.

"Reinforce it good and solid . . . he believes in hammering his points home!"

Joyful enthusiasm is one of the notable aspects of the Christian religion. Its expression, in the style of delivering sermons, varies widely. But the central theme is always the same . . . the wonderful promise, old but ever new, of forgiveness and salvation.

"Confounded chimes ruined my putt again! There must be some law against that kind of racket on Sunday!"

This disturbed gentleman is living in a free land—one where he may worship, or golf, on Sunday mornings. He chooses the latter, but benefits from the former. For a nation of churches, dedicated to Christian principles, provides him the decent, safe, and free environment in which to prosper . . . and pay his country club dues!

"I let th' wife . . . do our church-going . . .
Sunday's . . . my only day . . . to relax . . ."

Mighty strenuous relaxation. Just as physical re-
creation is necessary for a sound body, so spiritual
inspiration is necessary for a sound soul.

"No parking problems, and our church donations make the monthly payments on the set!"

This misguided gentleman seems to regard Christianity as a 'spectator sport', like football or baseball. Something to WATCH; but not something to be INVOLVED in. Devoid of sacrifice, financial and otherwise; devoid of fellowship and personal experience—that which remains is not Christianity . . . only a sad imitation.

"I don't get it. Pop thanks God for givin' us this food, then bawls Mom out about the grocery bills!"

To be consistent is a prime essential in teaching our children about God. He will never be real to them so long as what we SAY is in conflict with what we DO. The greatest responsibility we have, as parents, is trying to be a living example of the Christian principles which alone can give a firm foundation to our children's lives.

"Well frankly I didn't care much for your sermon today, either!"

In many isolated areas throughout the world, missionaries are this very moment ministering to those who would otherwise have remained in pagan darkness. Theirs is a labor of love, seldom acclaimed and often dangerous. Let us not forget, surrounded by our own snug and secure environment, how very much these dedicated Christians deserve our moral and financial support.

"I'm afraid they took your 'God Will Provide' sermon too literally!"

God IS able to provide—but only through the instruments of His divine Will. As Christians, we become those instruments, with the combined privilege and obligation to give freely of our material blessings, our time, and our talents.

"Rather have more time to think it over?"

Inasmuch as God prospers us, should we return His portion grudgingly? True financial distress can temporarily affect the amount we give; but let us not adopt such artificially high living standards that luxuries come to be regarded as 'necessities.' If we give only what can be easily spared, could we not carry such reasoning one step further and obey only those Commandments which do not inconvenience us?

"I'm preparing a sermon for those who CAN pay their pledges and won't. What's the ecclesiastical equivalent for 'stinker'?"

A rose by any other name would still be a rose. And the coining of a polite name for those people in this world who enjoy a "free ride" at the expense of their associates doesn't make their actions any more admirable. The overwhelming majority of people insist on carrying their own weight, unless some unforeseen financial emergency arises.

"Yes, 'God helps those who help themselves'. . . but not to the assets of the First National Bank!"

Man often gets tangled in his own wisdom. And he sometimes accords almost the status of Scripture to his own sayings. The proverb 'God helps those who help themselves' is true to only a limited degree. Most of us experience some critical time in our life when burdens become so heavy, and strength so meager, we must rely on God to do it all. This proverb, at such a time, can serve to dishearten rather than to encourage.

"Reverend, stuff your ears or get outa hearin'
range . . . quick!"

Such respect for the cloth is admirable. Some
laymen, however, act as though the clergy were wrap-
ped in a layer of insulating material marked 'Do Not
Disturb;' protecting its members from knowledge of
life's harsher realities. Yet the average pastor is
witness to more such 'realities' in a week than most
laymen encounter in years.

"Young lady, you'll not palm off any OLD Testament on me . . . show me the NEWEST in the store."

Obviously no student of the Bible, this lady must have a cavity in her library that needs filling. Unless we develop a regular daily habit of Bible study, we deny ourselves the guidance, truth and inspiration illuminating its every page.

"I wouldn't have missed **THAT** sermon for anything . . . two mispronounced words, a dangling participle, and three sentences ending with prepositions!"

It so happened the TOPIC of this 'ungrammatical' sermon was a stirring appeal for tolerance toward each other . . . something which would have helped this critical lady, had she bothered to listen. We cannot build ourselves up by tearing another down.

"But he IS our baby!"

The modern church nursery is equipped for most any contingency—except the one above. There is no longer any need for parents of the 'younger set' to deny themselves the weekly inspiration we all receive from worshipping together.

"Brace yourself, Reverend! Here comes Tex with some more new members!"

Tex is so interested in helping fill the pews, he's lost sight of one important fact . . . people cannot be 'roped' into becoming Christians. We can, and should, invite any friend not affiliated with a church to come and visit with us. But the decision must be entirely theirs. No amount of outward persuasion can replace this all-important personal commitment.

"Would you care to reconsider your veto of the budget allowance for termite extermination?"

To some, a church budget is an "unnecessary evil." Yet, no church can operate effectively and have a strong witness in the community without a sound operating budget. And any church which tries to skimp on the essentials of simple upkeep is not only shortsighted, but a reproach to the cause of Christ.

"I'm getting out of here. I just saw their budget!"

If even church mice are discouraged by the "bare cupboards" of this church's financial plans, what will be the result in outreach for this so-called "light-house" of the Gospel. Surely, the cause of Christ deserves a generous margin for reaching out to those who have never heard the wondrous story of the Gospel.

"Thanks, but our future's already provided for . . . geiger counter, short-wave radio, food, candies, survival kit . . ."

Everything these days seems calculated to keep our thoughts concerned with our material rather than our spiritual—destiny . . . More than ever before we need to keep in sharp focus the ONLY source of true and permanent security—Jesus Christ.

"Repeat after me . . ."

Looks like honest Joe has run into his toughest customer. Even misguided souls who profess no faith are extremely reluctant to treat lightly anything associated with the Bible. Its power is apart from man—its truths the result of divine inspiration.

"Well, I liked your sermon."

Perhaps the above is a bit far-fetched—but there
are those who put on 'mental ear-muffs' when a sermon
deals with their own shortcomings. We should attend
church, not to be patted on the back for our virtues,
but to be made aware of our shortcomings and need of
divine help.

"Hope it won't shake Ed's faith in human nature when he discovers that church budget pledge is signed in disappearing ink!"

Nothing like a good practical joke . . . in the right place. But a church fund drive is definitely NOT the right place. In fact, ALL areas of church financing deserve the most serious consideration on the part of every member. Because church giving has always been left to the dictates of EACH INDIVIDUAL CONSCIENCE, some may tend to dismiss it too lightly. But without MONEY to keep the 'boiler' hot, the many vital functions of a church would soon slow to a halt!

"Please don't awaken him. Sunday morning's his only chance to sleep late!"

Of all the reasons church members have 'invented' to explain their absence from worship service, the one quoted above comes close to being the most popular of all.

"I didn't realize you and the preacher were such close friends, John. He said you'd furnished him lots of good material for his sermons!"

We think the little woman is just getting a well-aimed dig. If it gets hubby out of bed hereafter in time for church then perhaps the end justified the means. The pastor wants to be left out of this kind of family argument, though as he uses source material for his sermons completely OUTSIDE his own flock!

"... now the choir is being seated, and the next voice you hear will be the Pastor's ..."

Women's hats are as charming as they are individual; except to the party in back trying to see around a 'sombrero', or over a 'skyscraper.' The bravest man quails at telling a woman which of her hats to wear, but silently applauds those who thoughtfully choose a going-to-church bonnet permitting maximum visibility.

"And now for the collection . . ."

A good trick, if you can do it. None should be denied the right of worship; but All who can should support their beliefs in dollars and cents. Christianity's existence has always depended upon those who gave PERSONALLY of their time, effort, and money.

"Listen, that window was all cracked up before our baseball hit it!"

The minister sees beautifully wrought stained glass . . . the boy sees only an old window, full of cracks. Here is a simple illustration to show the broad difference in points-of-view between Youth and Adult . . . a difference as old as Time. Let us always remember this fact in Christian training of our children, so that patience and understanding may bridge the gap between our two 'worlds'.

"Stedman's the name. We dropped by for a cozy little visit in behalf of our church."

The unsung heroes of the congregation—those loyal couples who fare forth to meet the stranger and bid him welcome to the fold. May their work be crowned with success and their aplomb remain unruffled despite cool receptions and scuttling feet.

"Where IS that Bible? The pastor and his wife will be here in ten minutes!"

We know where it OUGHT to be. Right on the living room table—and not simply for the sake of appearances either. The moment we consign our Bible to the attic or a dusty place on the bookshelf, we likewise consign a portion of our life to mediocrity. Far from being 'obsolete' or 'passe', the Bible is the most challenging book ever written. A well worn Bible is the best guarantee of an ever-new outlook.

"Just let my sermon run a teeny bit over twenty minutes . . .!!"

In days gone by, sermons often lasted for hours. The average modern-day sermon is one-tenth as long and ten times more effective. It is not the QUANTITY of words that determines the POWER of a message—Lincoln's Gettysburg Address contained slightly over two hundred and fifty words!

"May I have a moment to discuss your church pledge?"

Every church building program involves many problems. Few are solved this easily—with a bone from Smith's Meat Market. Fortunately the challenge always brings forth those whose tireless effort and unselfish generosity eventually overcome every obstacle.

"Shut up, will you! Now you've got ME all upset about those Russian missiles, too!"

Fear is highly contagious. Those not firmly anchored in their Christian faith may react in several ways. They may surrender to fear, or hide their heads in the sand like an ostrich, or try to build a secure fortress from material things. The Christian's security is his faith in an all-powerful, almighty God.

"THE BIBLE? Cedric Smith, what have you been up to?"

Something is out of perspective in any home where daily reading of the Bible is not common practice. For the Bible, and especially the New Testament, represents an infallible road-map of life. There are no dead ends, no wrong turnings, no detours for the man or woman who uses the Bible as a daily guide for the road ahead.

"See ya later, Gus. The church building fund ran outa money again."

If the program of the church depended upon your participation alone, how far would it get before being stranded like this project?

"Why d' you suppose the teacher got so upset when I said Goliath would've been a pushover for the Lone Ranger?"

Every generation has its retinue of childhood heroes; inspirational characters who always triumph over the evils of this world. But they can never replace the real flesh-and-blood heroes—the Davids and the Josephs—whose thrilling exploits flow from the Book of Books to inspire EVERY generation, down through the annals of time.

"Better change this announcement to read 'eminent lecturer will **HONOR** our church', not '**FILL** our pulpit'!"

Here is an outstanding example of diplomacy . . . an attribute all Christians MUST have . . . an attribute they must use OFTEN. And if we study the qualities that go to make up a 'diplomat,' isn't the principal quality simply an inborn ability to deal with others in a spirit of Christian kindness?

"Listen, I had to attend Sunday School and church when I was young and it didn't hurt ME any!"

Apparently it didn't do him much good, either. Otherwise, he would realize that this sort of negative approach to the church is almost sure to destroy any significance it might have for his son. Only by regular church attendance can parents hope to set such an example themselves that their children come to know the vital importance of its influence on their own lives. Active participation in church activities by every member of the family group is the only answer to true family unity. Of all the varied responsibilities that go with being a parent, this is undoubtedly the most important to the child's future.

"Bless Mama and Daddy . . . I'll talk to You later about Sis!"

Fortunate are the children raised in homes where they learn the habit of daily prayer early in life. For it will prove a comfort and source of strength all of their days. No earthly possessions provide an adequate substitute for the inward security resulting from a faithful prayerful partnership with God.

"Send me all your thin ones . . . he won't budge!"

Some day a church usher may uncover the answer to his thorniest problem—'What causes the fatal fascination for the aisle end of a pew?' Why do so many members gladly endure trampled toes and scuffed shoes rather than move further down? Ushers throughout the world await the answer . . . the answer that will ease their duties and improve their tempers!

"Th' strain is gettin' me down . . . how much longer do I hafta be good to get that bee bee gun?"

Some—and not just children, either—seem to regard prayer as a means of gratifying their own wishes. As though God were a 'Celestial Santa Claus.' Prayer is no labor-saving substitute for effort on our part. It is a seeking of Divine Guidance to properly direct the energies and intellect God gave us.